Book of Wine Cartoons

Featuring Cartoons from **THE NEW YORKER**

Galileo Galilei said,
"Wine is sunlight held together by water."

An exquisite thought conjuring an exquisite image.
We hope you enjoy this wonderful collection of
exclusive New Yorker *cartoons,*
adding a smile to your day and providing
amusing inspiration to gatherings at home.

"*Knock it off. I'll just have a glass of white wine.*"

"For that price I'd want it to love me in return."

"It just won this year's equivalent of the Nobel."

"*I think you'll find this little wine quite amusing, m'sieur.*"

"*Let me guess. You had it up to here with the world of business,
so you packed it all in and started your own winery.*"

"Some wine with your vest?"

AFTER THE BREAKUP OF

BACCHUS, INC.

Ed, God of Red Wine

Judy, Goddess of White Wine

Charles, God of Rosé

Bobbi Jo, Goddess of Sherry, Port, and Passover-Type Wines

Ray, God of Wine Coolers

"*This is actually quite good. Remember the first time you tried to order pizza?*"

"*That bottle with the little flowers on the label isn't one of those that are going through the roof, is it?*"

"That will be perfect. We have a lot to talk about."

"*As you may have guessed, Stu, I asked you over tonight for more than just a little wine and cheese.*"

"Wine! Men! Song!"

"The great is $54.99, and I do have a near-great for $23.99."

"We'd love to, but we had too much wine and cheese in the eighties."

"Ça suffit, good buddy!"

"Our best—rated over 700 in both Math and Verbal."

"Made with pride in our basement."

"Not much—just flushing out my arteries."

"*Charles, would you be my vintner?*"

"*Then the demons that drove me to Tangier to try to write fiction turned around and drove me to the Napa Valley to make wine.*"

"*That's between me and my vintner.*"

"You'll notice that I was born in 1968—a very prestigious year."

CHIANTIS IN TRANSLATION

"Village of Overworked Housewives"

Gorgeous Hill Town without Newspapers

Valley Teeming with Abandoned Refrigerators

crawford

"You grab the food—I'll grab the wine."

"And it was a good year for the Mets, too!"

"Barry made the wine. I made the cheese."

"Of course, not everybody can face this kind of responsibility."

"Excellent, but not fit for a king."

"It means taking a hefty pay cut, but I've decided to accept the position as god of wine."

"At your opening, I see that you had two glasses of wine, eight pieces of cheddar, eight crackers, and seventeen grapes. That, of course, will have to come off the top of your end."

"*I want to introduce you guys to what I feel is a really gifted young Zinfandel.*"

"We go to these things hoping to discover either a terrific new artist or a good, cheap, drinkable California white."

"This one's kerosene, the other's Chardonnay."

"*And what is your preference in wine—single or double figures?*"

"We're hoping for a really smooth wine here."

"This is a night for white wine."

"Here's one I know we had before, but I don't remember if we hated it or loved it."

"May I say, sir, the staff and I just knew you'd see through that Beaujolais."

"My compliments, Stefan. Marvelous wine, excellent reception."

"It's a little white wine Stuart brought back from Idaho. Are you game?"

"On second thought, I'll have sangria. I had rosé
the last time we buried the hatchet."

"Hey, Johnny—am I nuts, or does this have a hint of oak?"

"*Would you care to see our gasoline list, or do you know what you want?*"

"eBay '99."

"Can you recommend a large-breasted Burgundy with a big behind?"

SIPRESS

"My approach is nontraditional, but from a uniquely Western perspective."

"*This isn't just any old food wine. This is the foodies' food wine.*"

"I want Chardonnay, but I like saying 'Pinot Grigio.'"

FRENCH ARMY KNIFE

"And don't try to pull the old 'good wine steward, bad wine steward' routine."

"Typical trust-fund red from a vanity vintner."

"*Something drinkable right now.*"

"*Is Pinot Noir where you want to be?*"

"This is a big wine. I recommend you order some big food."

"*Sorry, but you're going to have to remind me who gets the red wine and who gets the white?*"

"*Haven't you ever seen California wine being made before?*"

"By the way, hon, great food, great wine, great you."

"If it's a California wine you wish, Mr. Larry will assist you."

"You serve an inferior wine, Ted, but you have a nice view of Peconic Bay."

"Might I suggest the most expensive wine and the most expensive dinner?"

"It's your friend who writes about wine."

"It's a full-bodied wine with hints of acrimony, partisanship, and moral outrage."

"What do you have in investment-grade reds?"

"We didn't have time to pick up a bottle of wine,
but this is what we would have spent."

"*Our house wine is abominable.*"

"Sure, they drank it—but did they get it?"

"Oh, Lord! Not another wine-and-cheese party!"

"*Am I the only guy at this table who goes back to when this stuff was two hundred and fifty dollars a bottle?*"

"*Citizen of the world, wine connoisseur, husband. I may be spreading myself too thin.*"

"And pick up a wine—something that goes with fish."

"We're in luck. It's white wine!"

"*Bigfoot? Never heard of him.*"

"All of a sudden he can't stand the taste of beer."

"*What we have here is a very together but laid-back Bordeaux.*"

"So you've read my books and you've brought wine. Good."

Index of Artists

Front cover: Leo Cullum
Front cover flap: Donald Reilly
Back cover: Victoria Roberts
Back cover flap: Edward Koren